The Night Ship

Written by
Helen Harvey

Illustrated by
Maria Kontogiorgou (maRik)

Ransom

Look at the night ship.

Up and down, up and down,
it bobs on the dark river.

Now you can go on deck.

Ring the bell! Let down the sail!
The night ship sets off.

The moon is big and near. The chill
air is thick with fog.

Look at the old man.

Fear hangs on his thin, worn coat.

He has a golden bell. He hums and his bell rings.

Look at the fair maid.

She has a velvet hood. You cannot look under the hood.

Look at the owl zoom in the air.

Under the big moon, the owl looks for its lair.

The night ship is odd, but there is a lot to see.

See, the old man begins to wail. His bell rings, high and pure.

See, the fair maid sighs and weeps. She sweeps off her hood.

You cannot look.

The owl zooms down to the deck. **Tap, tap** go its feet.

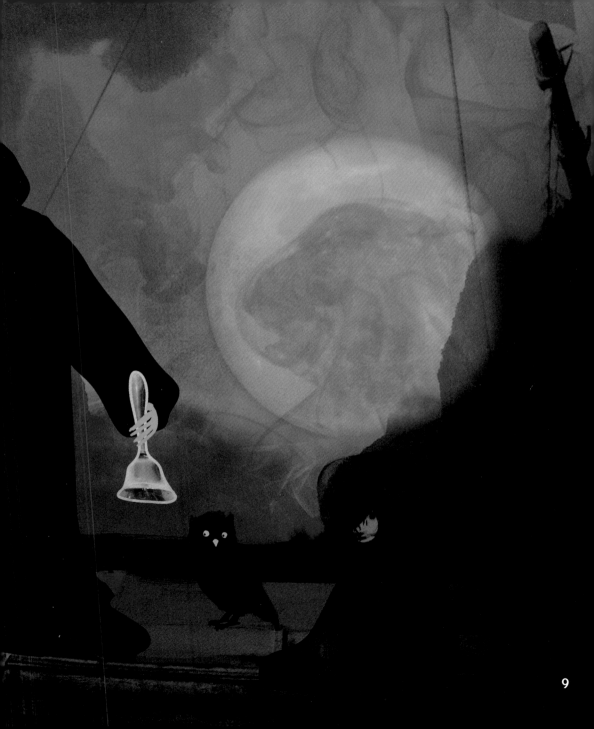

Now the fog is too thick.
Now the moon is too big.

The sea bobs up too high
and down too deep.

You may wish to get off the night ship.

We are too far down the river.

Now you cannot go back.
You can **never** go back.